Out and About Po

Chosen by John

Contents

OXFORD
UNIVERSITY PRESS

The Fair

I went to the fair.
I went on a train.
I went on a bus.
I went on a plane.

3

I went on a horse.
I won a brown bear.

I had lots of fun
When I went to the fair.

John Foster

At the Seaside

We went in the sea.
We had a good swim.
Tim splashed me.
I splashed him.

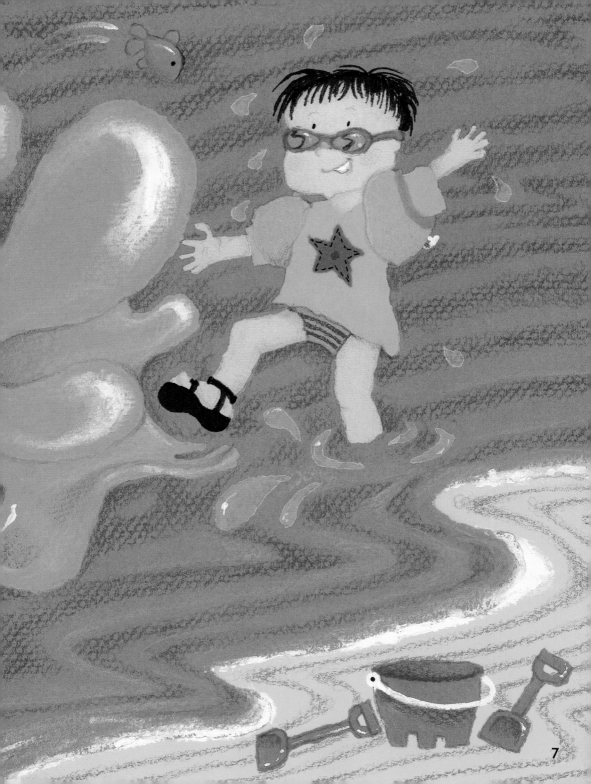

We dug in the sand.
We dug all day.

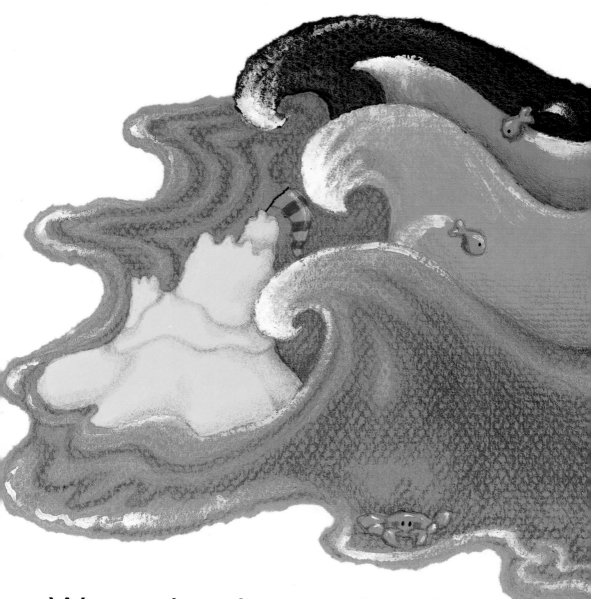

We made a big sandcastle.
The sea washed it away.

John Foster

Skip!

One skip, two skip
three skip, four,
five skip, six skip,
seven skip, more!

Eight skip, nine skip
ten skip, hop –
skip skip, skip skip,
skip skip, STOP!

Andrew Collett

You Can't Catch Me

Run round the swing
Run round the tree
Run round the slide
You can't catch me!

John Foster